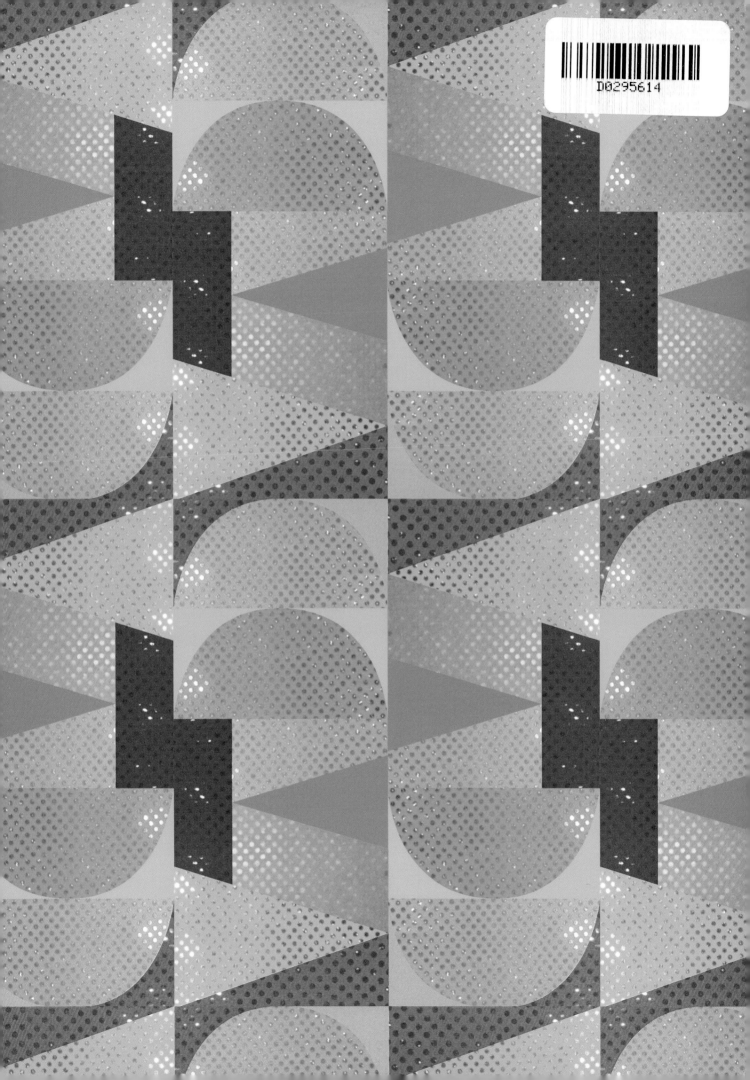

You will meet the Trolls:

Poppy

Branch

King Peppy

Cooper

Biggie (and Mr. Dinkles)

Guy Diamond

Maddy

DJ Suki

Harper

Satin & Chenille

Karma

Smidge

Creek

Cybil

Fuzzbert

And the Bergens:

Cloud Guy

King Gristle

Bridget

Chef

EGMONT
We bring stories to life

DreamWorks Trolls © 2018 DreamWorks Animation LLC.
All Rights Reserved.

Editorial content originated by
Egmont Creative Solutions, London/Warsaw
Cover Art: Karol Kinal
ISBN 978 1 4052 9121 7
68615/001
ID EGM18GLO0050-01

DreamWorks

Trolls

Annual 2019

This Troll-tastic Annual belongs to:

....

Write your name here

CONTENTS

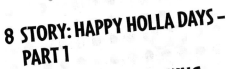

Annual 2019

STORY: Happy Holla Days

Part 1

One day, as King Gristle and Bridget were chilling in the throne room of the Bergen castle, a new greeting card arrived in the mail.

"It's a holiday card from Poppy!" Bridget cooed, opening the pink envelope.

"Another one?" grumbled Gristle. "If you ask me, those Trolls have way too many holidays. Like, every single day!"

"I think it's nice," Bridget said longingly. "Having so much to celebrate ..."

Meanwhile, in Troll Village, Poppy wondered why she never received a holiday card from her dear Bergen friends.

"It's like ever since the Bergens got rid of Trollstice –" she began, but Branch interrupted her.

"Which was good," he insisted, "because Trollstice was all about eating us!"

"True," Poppy agreed. "But now they have nothing to celebrate. Nothing to look forward to."

The thought of Bergens having nothing to celebrate made Poppy very sad, but then she had a wonderful, exciting idea! She spent the whole night working out the details of her plan, scrapbooking furiously. The next morning, she was ready to show Branch her scrapbook.

"I decided the Bergens need a new holiday!" she chirped. "No one knows holidays better than us Trolls, so we'll just give the Bergens one of our holidays! Brilliant, huh?"

"Bridget is my best friend," continued Poppy. "The Bergens should have a day of dancing and singing and costumes and presents ... and glitter!"

"Are you sure this is a good idea?" Branch asked.

"Absolutely!" Poppy said. "Let's make that holiday happen!"

"HOLIDAY!" several other Trolls chanted, popping up behind Branch and startling him.

"Looks like we're headed to Bergen Town!" Branch said, giving in to Poppy's plan.

The Trolls quickly prepared everything they needed and climbed onto a Caterbus. It looked like a huge caterpillar, with lots of sections and two antennae in front. Inside, however, it resembled a spacious, comfy bus, decorated in bright colours.

Poppy and Branch found a two-Troll seat near the front. Suddenly, Branch heard a familiar voice coming from the driver's seat ...

"Oh no," mumbled Branch, realising that their driver was Cloud Guy. "Not him."

White and puffy, Cloud Guy wore his usual striped gym socks, but he'd added a snappy blue-and-gold driver's cap with a black brim.

"Sit back, relax and feel the love. Next stop, Bergen Town ... Town ... Town," announced Cloud Guy, mimicking his own echo, and ... they were off!

Continues on page 34.

Holiday Scrapbooking

Poppy is going to make sweet scrapbook gifts for her friends.

She has cut out a lot of decorations, but she only needs to use 6 of them. Help Poppy find these elements in the artistic mess below.

○ ○ ○ ○ ○ ○

Every snowflake is absolutely unique. Help Poppy complete the second halves of these snowflakes.

14

Card for Bridget

The first holiday card is ready! Poppy prepared this for her friend Bridget, but then she decided to change some details.

Can you find 6 differences between these two cards? Every time you spot a difference, colour in a star.

☆ ☆ ☆ ☆ ☆ ☆

Do you know what Poppy wrote in the card for Bridget?

Cross out every **HOLLA** from the string of letters below, then write the remaining letters on the card to reveal her message.

HOLLAMILHOLLALIONHOLLAHUHOLLAGSFO RHOLLATHHOLLAEHOLIHOLLADAYSHOLLA!

__ __ __ __ __ __ __ __

__ __ __ __ __

__ __ __ __ __ __ __!

15

Answers on pages 68-69

Colourful Lights

It's time to prepare the Troll Village for a holiday – this needs a lot of colourful lights and decorations.

Guy Diamond is trying to find the chain with the most lights on it. Can you help him by following the lines and counting up the lights? Write the totals in the stars.

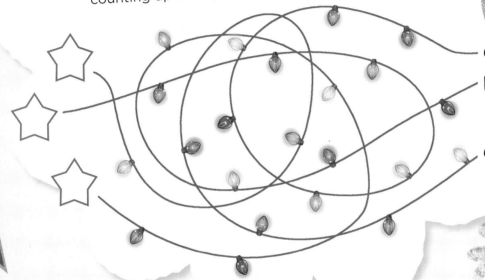

a.

b.

c.

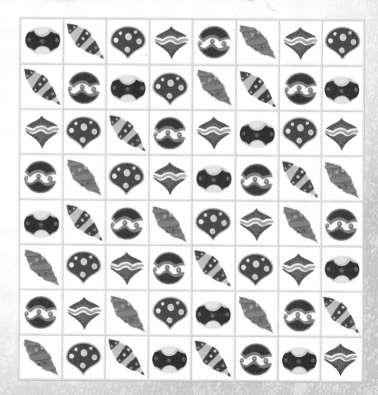

The Trolls made a lot of beautiful ornaments for the holiday.

Look for the decorations below in the grid opposite. Can you find them shown in the exact same sequence?

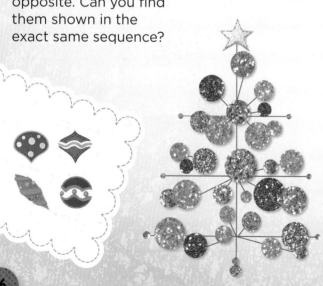

Answers on pages 68-69

Cloud Guy Code

The Trolls are going to get in Caterbus but Cloud Guy, the master of fist bumps and high fives, stops them - they can't go ahead until they solve his puzzle!

Help the Trolls crack the code of secret gestures and write down Cloud Guy's message in the frame below.

DECK   THE   HEY!   ON   TOP   PARTY

START

Hug Time!

Match each friend to his shadow so Poppy can hug all her friends.

a

b

Write down the number!

c

d

1   2   3   4

Friendly Memory Game!

Look carefully at the picture for approximately 3 minute, then turn over to answer the challenging questions about it.

Question time!

19

Friendly Memory Game!
Question Time!

2. Which Troll is behind Poppy?
~~~~~~~~~~~~~~~~~~~~

1. Which Troll is the tallest?

5. Which Troll is the smallest?
~~~~~~~~~~~~~~~~~~~~

4. Did you spot where Fuzzbert is?
~~~~~~~~~~~~~~~~~~~~

3. Who is Guy Diamond standing in front of?
~~~~~~~~~~~~~~~~~~~~

7. Who is between Cooper and Branch?
~~~~~~~~~~~~~~~~~~~~

6. Did you notice Branch? Where is he? ~~~~~~~~~~~~~~~~~~~~

9. Who is standing next to Fuzzbert?
~~~~~~~~~~~~~~~~~~~~

8. Is Mr. Dinkles wearing a hat?

10. who is glittery?
~~~~~~~~~~~~~~~~~~~~

If you answered all the questions correctly – brave, you are Troll-tastic!

If you answered half the questions – you need to work on your concentration skills.

If you answered less than 5 questions – turn back and try the activity again!

Puzzles!

Can you match the little pictures below to the spaces in the big picture?

a   b   c   d

Do you know who King Gristle loves? Write her name below:

B _ _ _ _ _ _ _

my friends

Satin and Chenille

Satin and Chenille are very original, aren't they? They are not your average twins – they are connected by their colourful hair!

This is the Fashion Twins' Super Threads boutique, the place where fashion magic happens! Satin and Chenille measure, cut and make outfits for Troll Village's most spectacular events, but it's street style that's really their thing. We Troll girls really love their sense of style!

1. Can you count how many dresses are hanging here?
2. Can you spot who is hiding between the rolls of fabric on the left?

The thing that brings them together is FASHION! Satin and Chenille know what trends are blooming right now. Everyone would love to look like them especially as they never, ever wear the same outfit at the same time! I admire them so much!

Who stands between the sisters? Can you guess?

When it's Hug Time, Satin and Chenille always (t)win – they are always there to give each other a hug! And if you want to hug them, you always get an extra hug. It's double the hug with the Fashion Twins!

b

a

Whom do these styles belong to?

c

23

Answers on pages 68-69

CONTINUES ON PAGE 58.

27

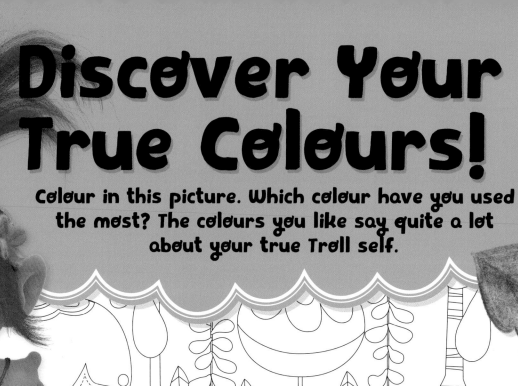

Discover Your True Colours!

Colour in this picture. Which colour have you used the most? The colours you like say quite a lot about your true Troll self.

28

Green: you enjoy peace, harmony and nature. If you want to relax, you just put your boots on and head straight to the park or forest.

Blue: you are all about having a sense of security. You don't like being stressed out and in your free time you take artsy photos or paint. Blue is the colour of artists!

Violet: you like everything to be well-organised because mess gives you a headache. Sometimes you like being by yourself and enjoying the silence. You are reflective and value spiritual growth.

SO, IF YOU ARE TEAM:

Yellow: you are creative and full of energy. You always have a smile on your face and come up with original ideas.

Pink: you probably fall in love quite often. Pink-thusiasts are very emotional and friendly, they are also great companions. It's always fun spending time with them.

Red: you are energetic, active and believe in yourself. You have all the traits of a winner and that is exactly who you are! You enjoy taking the lead role and being in a room full of friends is your natural environment!

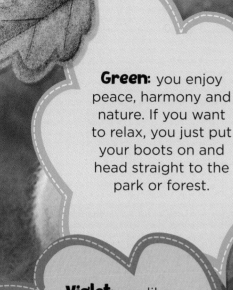

Harper's tips!

If you need more energy, surround yourself with yellow, orange and red!

You feel sleepy or just too hot? Try wearing a blue T-shirt or paint a piece of paper blue and place it in front of you. This is the best way to refresh your Troll self!

Want to relax? Go for a walk in the forest or a park and wear a green sweater. Green is the best colour for all stressed Trolls.

About the Bergens!

Here's a quiz about the Bergens! What is that smell? It's Bergen Town. Test your knowledge of their world!

2. King Gristle likes eating ...

a broccoli

b pizza

1. What does Chef always carry with her ...

a a handbag

b a bumbag

3. Bridget wears ...

a bunches

b plaits

4. King Gristle burns calories on:

a a bicycle

b a treadmill

5. Bridget and Gristle like going:

a running together

b roller skating

. The Bergen hef is usually:

a cheerful

b miserable

7. What colour is Bridget's bedroom?

a blue

b pink

8. What grows in the centre of Bergen Town?

a Troll Tree

b Troll Flower

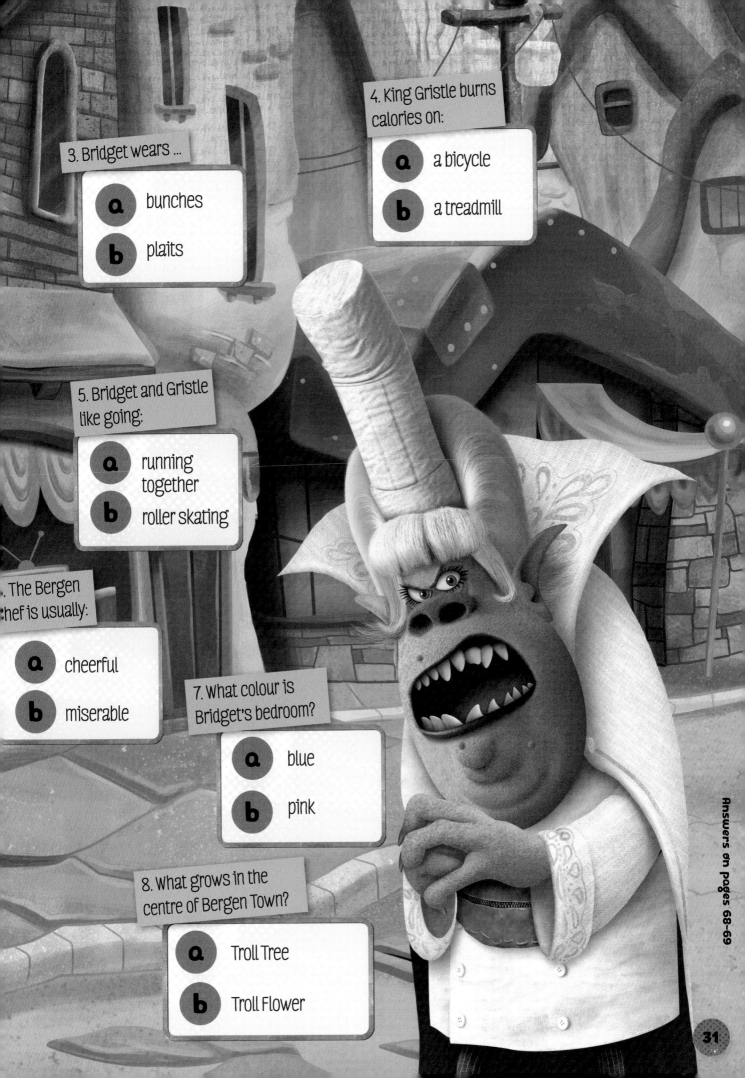

Answers on pages 68-69

The Great Escape
from Bergen Town

How to play:
Roll the dice and move forward the number you roll. The first to the finish wins!

Help the Trolls run away from Bergen Town. Roll the dice and follow the instructions. Good luck!

You end up on the Troll Tree. You'll be safe again when you roll a 6.

You eat too many cupcakes. Go back to Branch's Bunker to rest for 1 turn.

You hide in Branch's Bunker. Miss a turn.

Are you hungry for a cupcake? Someone has left one for you! Go on 1 space.

START

Oh no, a Bergen appears. You freeze and lose a turn.

The Trolls need your help. Go back to the closest pod and wait for them. Miss a turn.

You hide in a Pod – a safe hideout from the Bergens. Miss a turn.

Poppy has fallen asleep and you have to carry her. Miss 2 turns.

Hug Time! Roll the dice again!

Lucky you! Move forward 3 places.

FINISH! HOORAY, YOU ARE SAFE NOW!

STORY: Happy Holla Days

Part 2

After a crazy, bumpy ride through a wormhole, the Trolls finally reached the Bergen castle. Bridget was thrilled to see her best friend, Poppy.

"What are you doing here, Poppy?" she asked.

"We came to give you one of our holidays!" Poppy explained.

"Holiday?" Bridget repeated, still confused. "Why do we need a holiday?"

"Hit it!" shouted Poppy. Right on cue, the Trolls started the music.

Singing and dancing, the Trolls presented holiday after holiday – Glitterpalooza! Tickle Day! Lasers and Foam Day! Balloon Squeal Day! – and when that didn't work, they shared even more fun and amazing Troll holidays and celebrations.

"Epic Hug Ball Day!" shouted the Trolls, performing wildly. "Shock a Friend Day! Express Yourself Day! Socks Day! Keep It to Yourself Day! Fireworks Day! Fuzzy Onesie Day!" they went on.

"STOP!" Bridget finally cried. "None of this really means anything to us."

"Right," Poppy said, nodding. "How about Pick a Friend's Nose Day? Or ..."

"Poppy, enough!" Bridget interrupted her. "You're not listening to me! I think maybe you should go."

Stunned and hurt, Poppy turned and ran out of the room.

Moments after the Trolls left, a sudden realisation dawned on Bridget. After all, the Bergens had one good reason to celebrate – a Troll-tastic reason, one may add!

With Gristle's help, Bridget fashioned a brand-new and completely different holiday and shared it with Poppy and her friends. The Trolls and the Bergens celebrated together, singing festive songs and skating on the ice under the beautifully decorated Troll Tree.

"I'm sorry, Bridget," Poppy said, finally realising her mistake. "I should have listened to you. I got so caught up in telling you what to celebrate that I didn't even think about why you'd want to celebrate ..."

"That's all right," Bridget said, smiling. "Holidays are about celebrating the awesome things in life. So we're celebrating our friendship with the Trolls!"

"A friendship like ours is definitely worth celebrating!" exclaimed Poppy and she gave Bridget a big hug.

As gentle snow began to fall, sparkling magically in the colourful lights, the Bergens and the Trolls joined together to sing a happy song about celebrating their new holiday: Bergen-Troll Friendship Day! And everybody agreed that it was the best holiday EVER!

THE END

HOLLA

Festive Tree

Look! The Trolls prepared a tree to celebrate the holidays – doesn't it look magical and really festive?

Every decoration is different, but wait ... one of them appears twice! Can you spot the pair?

Answers on pages 68-69

Let's Celebrate!

Time for presents! Help the friends put the right gifts in the empty places, but remember that every present can only appear once in every row and column.

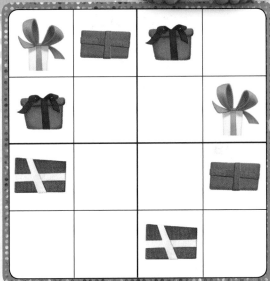

1   2   3   4

At the holiday party

the most stylish twins ever, Satin and Chenille, look totally glamorous! They take a lot of photos, but only one matches the original. Can you find it?

a

b

c

Answers on pages 68-69

Presents for Everyone!

The Trolls can hardly wait to receive their gifts! Match each present to the right troll by using the first letter of his or her name, which is written on the present tags.

S

P

B

C

Who is the biggest present for? It's for you! Write the first letter of your name on the tag and think about what you'd like it to be.

Bergen Town!

Can you spot 10 differences between these two pictures of Bergen Town?

Which of Chef's stylish lamps is the odd one out?

1

2

3

4

How did YOU do?

Less than 3 minutes:

You've got a wonderful pair of eyes! Don't tell Chef, or she might want to use them in her latest stew.

More than 3 minutes:

Well done, a thorough job. You might have taken a little longer, but you got there in the end!

45

Answers on pages 68-69

Create your own TROLL BAND

Design the most Troll-tastic band EVER!

The Trolls I'd love to have in my band are:

Poppy

Branch

Cooper

Biggie

DJ Suki

Creek

Guy Diamond

Satin & Chenille

Smidge

Roll 2 dice to choose a word from each list. Then put them together to make your Troll band name.

List 1:
1: Troll-tastic
2: Hair-mazing
3: Poptimistic
4: Sparkly
5: Huggable
6: Glittery

List 2:
1: Cupcakes
2: Rainbows
3: Diamonds
4: Snack Pack
5: Boop!
6: Hair heroes

My band NAME is ...

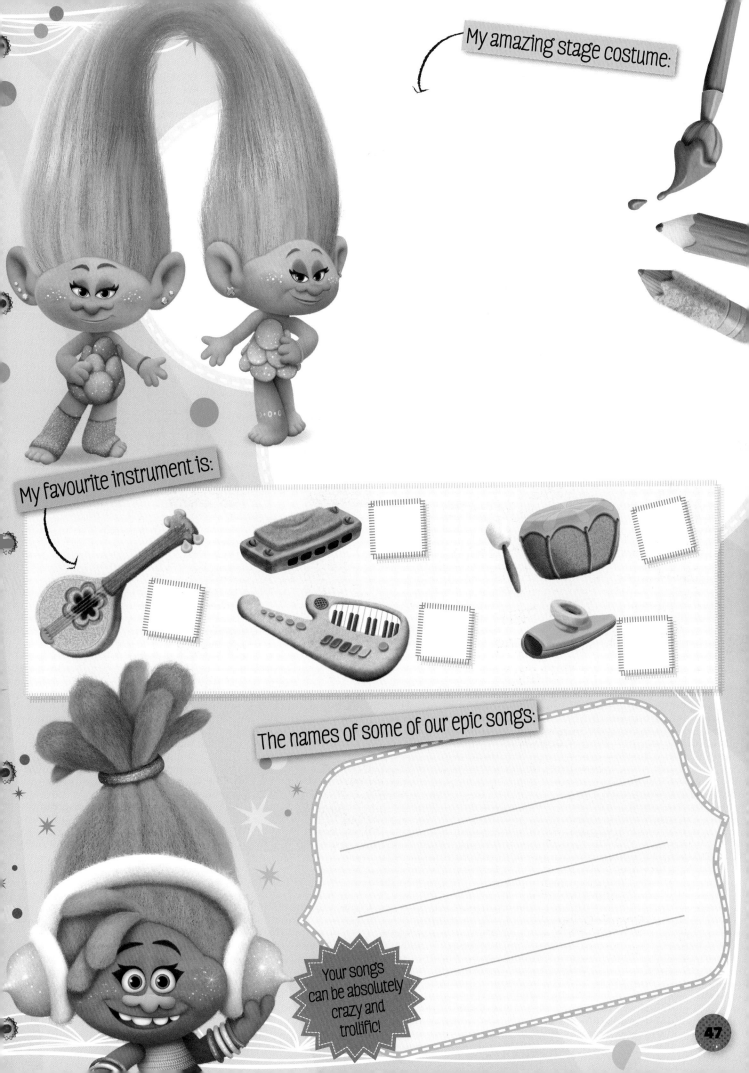

My amazing stage costume:

My favourite instrument is:

The names of some of our epic songs:

Your songs can be absolutely crazy and trollific!

Lost and Found!

Oops, Cooper has lost his favourite harmonica and Poppy's cowbell in this pile of musical instruments. Help him find them!

This is what they look like!

Answers on pages 68-69

What's in your Stars?

Feeling mystic? Cybil has taken a look into the future and this is what's in store for you!

Find your birth month in the chart below to read your fortune!

January

Your symbol: The Tarantapuff!

Your fortune: This month will start well, you'll find an unopened pack of gummy sweets under a cushion. The next day a dog will run off with them!

February

Your symbol: The Glowfly!

Your fortune: Take care when putting on your jumper. It once took me three hours to figure out what was wrong with mine – it was a pair of pants.

March

Your symbol: The Chorusfly!

Your fortune: Just like your symbol, your month will be, er, stripy. Make the most of it by becoming a mime artist and wearing a stripy mime top.

April

Your symbol: The Sparkbug!

Your fortune: Don't forget to turn the lights off when you leave a room. Wasting electricity harms the planet and costs money.

May

Your symbol: The Fuzzy Wuzzbert!

Your fortune: If someone you know is feeling blue send them some flowers. If they are happy send them some twigs.

June

Your symbol: The Chanter!

Your fortune: Spend today acting like Biggie. Wear a vest and dress up a worm with a jaunty hat.

July

Your symbol: The Glitterbug!

Your fortune: Nothing you read will make sense this month. Eventually you'll work out the problem. You've been holding books upside-down!

August

Your symbol: The Spider!

Your fortune: Look up there! What is that? Is it some sort of bird? Oh wait, it's nothing. Never mind.

September

Your symbol: The Bluebug!

Your fortune: This month stay away from ants' nests. They bite and get in your clothes. Believe me!

October

Your symbol: The Butterfly!

Your fortune: Try spending the day with an orange on your head. If anyone asks what you're doing, tell them you're trying to get a balanced diet.

November

Your symbol: The Songbloom!

Your fortune: You will learn a new language today. Tomorrow you will forget everything you learned. That's life!

December

Your symbol: The Critterbug!

Your fortune: Next week you will get a fortune cookie with a much better fortune in it than this one!

My friend

MADDY

Look at her HAIR-mazing hairdo! Isn't it fantastic?

What I love about Maddy is that she is not just a great hairdresser, she is also hair-larious!

She styles and shapes her hair into amazing creations. This is real art!

This is all she needs to make the Trolls' true colours shine!

We wouldn't look so good if it wasn't for Maddy's talent! She is the one who takes care of our hair and she knows all the tricks of the trade.

Trolls have magical hair and Maddy makes it look even more magical, just look at Guy Diamond's spectacular do!

Maddy is in a dream team with Satin and Chenille, two funky fashion designers and experts about when, how, why and what to wear. The three of them create wonderful styles!

Check out Maddy's awesome hair salon!

Colour Maddy's hair salon in bright colours!

As a hairstylist, Maddy often hears good news first and she loves to share it with everyone! Think of something really great about one of your friends and write it here.

HAIR STUDIO!

This is where all hair-mazing dreams come true! What are the hairstyles the Trolls go for?

with Maddy

Select the perfect hairstyle for each Troll and make their visit to Maddy's hair studio a Trollificent experience!

Poppy – this Troll girl loves pink, but maybe it's time for a change? At least try spicing her style up with unique hair accessories!

DJ Suki – she could try streaks of colour, don't you think? Try to give her an amazing look!

Guy Diamond – this Troll wants even more glitter in his hair. Maybe you will add some sparkle to his Troll-style by plaiting his hair with colourful stars?

Satin and Chenille – this is double the trouble, because both Troll girls need to like the new hairstyle. Maybe you should go for hair-mazing accessories? Or maybe you should give the Fashion Twins amazing rainbow-coloured hair?

Fuzzbert – he really likes his hairstyle but recently, he was considering adding different coloured highlights. What do you think?

Cooper - his dreadlocks are cool, but this time Cooper would like plaits. Use your inner creative Troll to draw and colour the plaits using all your brightest colours!

Salon Spot

It's been a crazy day in the hair salon! Can you find the equipment below to help Maddy tidy up?

1 x		1 x	
2 x		2 x	
3 x		3 x	
4 x		4 x	

Can you help untangle the hairbands and work out how many of each colour there are?

Pizza Puzzle

Bridget has used a pizza to hide a message for King Gristle from Chef! Can you work out what it says?

START here!

FINISH here!

Follow the circle in a clockwise direction and write down every third letter in the spaces below to reveal the message.

m_ _ _ _ _ _ _ _

_ _ _ _ _ _ _ _

_ _ _ _ _ _ _ _ _ _ _ '

Find your real Troll Talent

What are you good at? What would you like to do in the future? Check out this quiz, as it might help you find your true colours!

1. How do you like to spend your free time?

- dancing and singing
- drawing
- hairstyling
- playing sports or climbing
- cooking
- reading fashion magazines or trying on new dresses

2. It's Saturday morning and you don't have to go to school! What are your plans?

- checking out new hairstyles.
- shopping!
- opening my scrapbook and writing and drawing for as long as possible!
- see if my friends want to go swimming!
- opening my cookery book and making some cupcakes!
- organising a party.

3. Your best present:

- a new hairdo
- a new scrapbook
- dancing lessons or a climbing rope.
- book about sweets, cakes, etc.
- a new dress or a make-up box
- a heavy metal album

4. Your dream job:

- a fashion designer
- a DJ, singer, or a dancer
- a chef
- participating in the Olympics one day would be great!
- an illustrator or writer
- a hair stylist

5. Your favourite character is:

- Maddy
- Satin and Chenille
- Poppy
- Guy Diamond
- Biggie
- Smidge

w pick the cupcake that appears most often on your answers and check your results.

You love to write, draw, and create, just like Harper and Poppy. Maybe a writing career is ahead of you, or graphic design. Think about it and draw, read and write as much as you can, that's your stuff!

It seems obvious that you love dancing, music and rhythm. Maybe it is time to think about dancing lessons? Or to record your own album? Wouldn't it be great? DJ Suki or Cooper are your true Troll match.

You love cooking and eating – life would be sad without sweets. But be smart and don't eat too many. Healthy foods can taste just as good.

Swimming pools, sports, climbing – you love them all. There is no better place for them than the Olympics! Like Smidge, eat healthily and don't forget to train! Sports are your true passion.

That's hair-mazing! You love hair and trying fun and different hairstyles! Fuzzbert and Maddy, our hair master, would be proud of you. Keep practising but don't forget – hairstyles are all about fun!

You can't hide it! You're a fashionista! Satin and Chenille welcome you to their world! Glittery Guy Diamond adds lots of sparkle to the fashion scene. Experiment with styles and dance moves just like these funky Trolls and you'll be ready to party in no time!

59

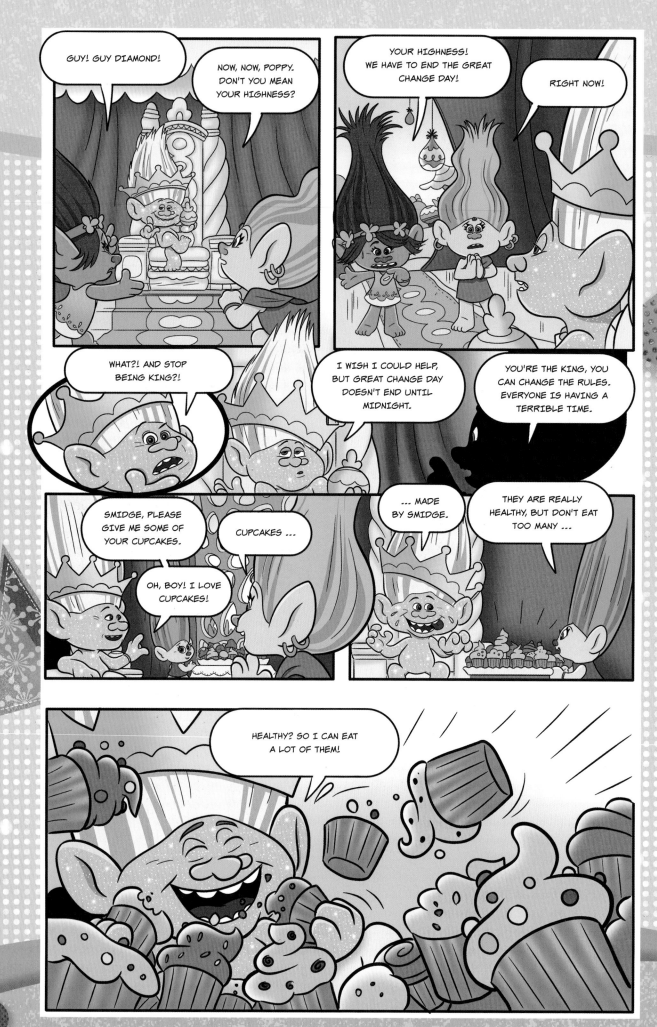

My friend
GUY DIAMOND

Everyone in Troll Village knows Guy Diamond – he's the happiest, shiniest Troll around!

Guy enjoys Hug Time almost as much as I do!

We did think about making Guy Diamond some clothes, but his true colours are just so shiny! He thinks being covered in glitter is the best outfit anyway!

Who needs a glitterball at a party when Guy Diamond is around?

Guy Diamond always knows how to kick off a party. He loves working on new dance moves.

Additional photography © Shutterstock.com

Guy Diamond leaves a trail of glitter wherever he goes.

Guy Diamond leaves glitter on everything he touches and everyone he hugs.

Actually, Guy just kind of leaves glitter EVERYWHERE!

Guy Diamond and Branch get on really well. They even lived together when Guy's roof collapsed in a glitter storm!

Guy helped with the glitter surprise in my coronation invitations.

a

b

c

He's so shiny that he can glitter up anything. Can you tell who he's sparkled?

63

Answers on pages 68-69

FIND YOUR Troll BFF!

Want to know who your bestest Troll buddy ever would be? Do this quiz!

START

What word best describes you?

COOL I'M TOTALLY HIP AND HAPPENING.

CALM I'M SUPER CHILLED OUT.

FUN! I MAKE PEOPLE LAUGH ALL THE TIME.

Do you like helping people?

MAYBE BUT I NORMALLY THINK OF MYSELF FIRST.

YEAH! I LOVE HELPING MY FRIENDS.

Which is your favourite fruit?

ORANGES NOM NOM NOM NOM NOM.

APPLES YUM YUM YUM YUM YUM.

Which of these would you like to play?

DRUMS BA-DUM-TISH!

GUITAR NEOW-WHOCKA WAHWAH!

Would you rather have ...

A HUG CUDDLES RULE!

A CUPCAKE I'M SO HUNGRY RIGHT NOW!

Which colour do you like best?

RED LIKE TULIPS, LOVE HEARTS AND LAVA.

BLUE LIKE THE SKY AND THE SEA.

Which of these critters is creepier?

ARGH!
A TARANTAPUFF!

EEK!
BARNABUS!

Guy Diamond is your Troll BFF! Just like him you can't help but sparkle all the time!

Which is your favourite?

DARKNESS
PERFECT FOR HIDING AND BEING ALONE.

GLITTER!
WHO DOESN'T WANT TO SPARKLE AND SHINE?

Which of these Trolls would you invite to your party?

COOPER
HE CAN BRING HIS HARMONICA AND GET EVERYONE DANCING!

BIGGIE
HE GIVES AWESOME HUGS AND HE'D BRING MR. DINKLES!

Branch is your Troll BFF! You like hanging out in dark places and so does he!

Where are you happiest?

IN MY BUNKER!
IT'S BERGEN-PROOF AND POPPY-PROOF.

AT A PARTY!
WITH ALL MY BUDDIES.

Poppy is your Troll BFF! You're the life and soul of the party, just like her!

Which of these critters is cuter?

THE SPIDER!
DAAW, WHAT A SWEETIE!

THE CRITTERBUG!
JUST LOOK AT ITS FACE!

What's more important?

MUSIC
YOU'RE RIDING ON A RAINBOW AND IF SOMEONE KNOCKS YOU OVER, YOU'LL JUST GET BACK UP AGAIN!

FRIENDS
YOU AND YOUR BEST BUDS ALWAYS COME FIRST.

DJ Suki is your Troll BFF! You're both mad about music – any time, any place, anywhere!

65

Trøll Teasers!

Get your clever hair on to solve these tricky teasers!

POPPY'S Pretty Perplexing Puzzle!

How many differences are there between these two pages of Poppy's scrapbook?

Tick the box!

1 ☐   2 ☐   3 ☐   4 ☐

HARPER Gets Her Paint On!

Tick the box!

Finish off Harper's picture. Who is she painting?

Poppy ☐

Branch ☐

Creek ☐

Smidge ☐

BIGGIE'S Big Beautiful Bewildering Befuddler!

Biggie wants a flower for Mr. Dinkles! Which path leads to it?

a
b
c
d

Tick the box!

a ☐ b ☐ c ☐ d ☐

Guy Diamond has got his glitter on! Which glitter splodge is Branch under?

1 2 3 4

Tick the box!

1 ☐ 2 ☐ 3 ☐ 4 ☐

GUY DIAMOND Does his Glitter Thing!

Which colour box have you ticked the most?

SING IT OUT!

purple! pink! yellow! green!

Answers

Page 18: Hug Time!
a – 4, b – 2, c – 3, d – 1.

Page 20: Question Time!
1. Cooper; 2. Biggie; 3. Satin and Chenille;
4. On the left; 5. Smidge; 6. On the right;
7. DJ Suki; 8. Yes; 9. Smidge; 10. Guy Diamor

Page 21: Puzzles!

1 – c, 2 – b, 3 – d, 4 – a. BRIDGET.

Pages 22-23: Satin and Chenille
1 – 2 dresses. 2 – Fuzzbert. Maddy is
between the sisters. a – Biggie,
b – Cooper, c – DJ Suki.

Pages 30-31: About the Bergens!
1 – b, 2 – b, 3 – a, 4 – b, 5 – b, 6 – b, 7 – b, 8 – a

Page 40: Festive Tree

Page 41: Let's Celebrate!

Photo **b** matches the original.

Page 14: Holiday Scrapbooking

Page 15: Card for Bridget

Poppy's message for Bridget:
MILLION HUGS FOR THE HOLIDAYS!

Pages 16: Colourful Lights
a – 9, b – 7, c – 6. **a** has the most lights.

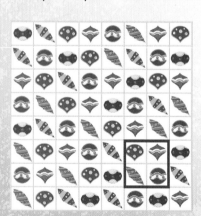

Page 17: Cloud Guy Code
HEY! PARTY ON THE TOP DECK.

Page 42: Presents for Everyone!

 – Smidge   – Branch

– Poppy   – Cooper

Page 45: Bergen Town!

Lamp **2** is the odd one out.

Page 48: Lost and Found!

Page 54: Salon Spot

There are 6 blue hairbands and 7 green hairbands.

Page 55: Pizza Puzzle

Meet me at Captain Starfunkle's.

Pages 63: Guy Diamond

a - Cooper, b - Smidge, c - Branch.

Pages 66-67: Troll Teasers!

There are 4 differences in Poppy's Puzzle. Harper is painting Creek. Biggie should take path **c** to get the flower. Branch is hidden under glitter splodge **1**. Most answers are green.